SPELLING

RULES and PRACTICE 2

Susan J. Daughtrey M.Ed.

Childs World Education Limited
Revised 2005

CONTENTS

SYLLABLES

Every word in the English language can be divided into syllables. **A syllable is a small part of a word that is pronounced as a unit**. To decide how many syllables there are in a word, it is often a good idea to clap your hands to see how many 'beats' there are in a word. These 'beats' are the syllables. For example the word *car/pet* has 2 syllables, *el/e/phant* has three syllables and *in/for/ma/tion* has four syllables.

Upon examination of the syllables, one can see that **every syllable has one vowel sound**. This may be a single vowel, (the letter *y* is often considered a vowel), or a vowel digraph. **A *vowel digraph* comprises two vowels together which make one vowel sound**, such as *ai* in tr*ai*n, *oa* in s*oa*p, *ee* in sp*ee*ding and *ui* in fr*ui*t. A *silent e* is often discounted as it tends to be a vowel that is doing a job rather than making its own vowel sound.

Exercise One:_____

Underline each vowel sound in the words that follow. Use only one line under a *vowel digraph*, remember *y* can act as a vowel, and that *e* at the end of a word does not make a sound, but rather has a job to do, so ignore it when underlining. Say each word and listen to the 'beats' of the word. Then, alongside each word, write how many *syllables* there are in it.

complete	____	particular	____	independent	____	birthday	____
beckon	____	different	____	stressing	____	magnificent	____
information	____	geranium	____	instrument	____	satisfaction	____
expect	____	private	____	knowledge	____	invention	____
arrival	____	magical	____	carpenter	____	kitten	____

Dividing a word into syllables will help you with both reading and spelling. Let us look then at splitting up words into their syllables.

1. If there is a double letter in a word, you should divide between the two letters.

Example:

ladder	=	lad / der
sitter	=	sit / ter
tunnel	=	tun / nel

Exercise Two: _____

Divide these words into syllables. They all have double letters in them, so remember to divide them between the two letters.

bottom	_____ _____	better	_____ _____	sitter	_____ _____
barren	_____ _____	cotton	_____ _____	litter	_____ _____

dapper _____ _____   settee _____ _____   kennel _____ _____

summer _____ _____   bigger _____ _____   quarrel _____ _____

willow _____ _____   shutter _____ _____   wallow _____ _____

Let us look at one of the words above: *litter*

The two *tt*'s have a vowel on either side of them.

When a word has two consonants with one vowel on each side of them, the word is divided between the two consonants.

litter   =   lit / ter

2. In the same way we can split any two-syllable word which has two different consonants in the middle and a vowel on either side of them.

Example:

banker   =   ban / ker
sister   =   sis / ter
magnet   =   mag / net

Exercise Three: _____

Divide these words into *syllables*, splitting each word between the two consonants.

concert _____   window _____   carpet _____

garden _____   stagnant _____   enjoy _____

master _____   forbid _____   tablet _____

curtain _____   under _____   chimney _____

picture _____   pencil _____   handbag _____

In words of more than one syllable, one of the syllables is emphasised more strongly than the others. For example, do we say WINdow or winDOW? It is WINdow and we show this by placing a small mark called a *stress mark* at the end of the strongly emphasised syllable. Like this:

window   =   win′ dow

3. To help with reading, a small mark, called a *stress mark*, is used to show that one syllable is emphasised more strongly than another. It is placed at the end of the most important syllable.

NOTE:

In general, the first syllable of an English word is *stressed* unless the word begins with a *prefix*.

Example:

	circus	=	cir′ cus
	monster	=	mon′ ster
BUT	*ex*pose	=	*ex* pose′
	*pre*tend	=	*pre* tend′

Exercise Four: _____

Say these words aloud. Then divide these words into *syllables* between the two consonants. Rewrite, marking the strongly emphasised syllable with a *stress mark*.

garden	_____	forget	_____	compose	_____
invade	_____	concern	_____	hamster	_____
tractor	_____	shipment	_____	confess	_____
sorrow	_____	inspect	_____	crimson	_____
expect	_____	tennis	_____	address	_____

A *CLOSED* SYLLABLE

4. If a syllable ends in a consonant, it is referred to as a CLOSED SYLLABLE. In a *closed syllable* the vowel sound is *short*. It is 'cut off' by the consonant.

Example:

carpet	=	car′pet
ladder	=	lad′ der
shipment	=	ship′ment

In each case, the vowel is 'closed off' by a consonant causing its sound to be *short*.

Exercise Five: _____

Create a sensible word by adding another syllable of your own to each of the following *closed* 'starter' syllables. Place the *stress mark* next to the strongly stressed syllable.

Example:

im + press	=	im press′
com + pare	=	com pare′

con	_____	sin	_____	com	_____	sup	_____
or	_____	ad	_____	im	_____	mis	_____
fan	_____	man	_____	dis	_____	sub	_____

ban	_____	in	_____	for	_____	rob	_____
spar	_____	can	_____	op	_____	min	_____

A vowel will always be *short* and say its *sound* unless we do something to it to make it *long* and so say its *name*. There are several ways we can achieve this.

To make a vowel *long* and so say its *name* we can:

1. Add a *silent e* to the end of the word.

Example:

$$mat + e \quad = \quad mate$$
$$pop + e \quad = \quad pope$$

2. Place two vowels together to create a *vowel digraph*.

A *vowel digraph* is when two vowels next to each other make one vowel sound. It is usually the first of the two vowels that makes the sound. *Ai, oa, ie, ee, ea* and *ue* are *vowel digraphs* and in each word below the vowel sound is *long* and so says its *name*.

Example:

Tr*ai*n
S*oa*p
T*ie*

3. Another reason for a vowel to be *long* is the position of the vowel in the syllable.

AN *OPEN* SYLLABLE

5. An open syllable ends in a vowel and the vowel sound is *long*.

Example:

silent	=	si / lent
secret	=	se / cret
driver	=	dri / ver
stupid	=	stu / pid

In all these cases the first syllable is an *open* syllable ending in a vowel which therefore makes a *long* vowel sound. (The second syllable is *closed*, ending in a consonant and making a *short* vowel sound.)

(Note: In words which end in *ble, kle, tle, ple* and other *le* endings, the *le* ending is a separate syllable. These occur in a great number of words.)

Example:

crumble	=	crum / ble
sparkle	=	spar / kle
puzzle	=	puz / zle
stable	=	sta / ble

Exercise Six:_____

Mark the vowels in each of the syllables below with a *breve* ˘ for a *short* vowel sound, or a *macron* ˉ
for a *long* vowel sound. Write *open* or *closed* next to the syllable. Saying the syllable aloud will help.

in	_____	sin	_____	mo	_____	ma	_____
sta	_____	lo	_____	ad	_____	cra	_____
sis	_____	car	_____	spi	_____	fit	_____
pro	_____	con	_____	can	_____	scrib	_____
sec	_____	re	_____	sub	_____	spar	_____
trans	_____	fa	_____	por	_____	fol	_____
mad	_____	stu	_____	han	_____	com	_____
hu	_____	hun	_____	win	_____	ca	_____

Can you add another syllable to each of the 'starter' syllables above to make a sensible two-syllable
word? Write each of the words you create below. Say aloud each of the above open or closed 'starter'
syllables, pronouncing the vowel correctly before choosing another syllable to add to it. If you cannot
think of any endings yourself, here are some endings that will fit. Use any ending more than once if
necessary.

vent   lent   tion   ter   der   ker   dle   pet   tect
dent   ness   man   ger   low   ject   kle   it   ble   ment

_____
_____
_____
_____
_____
_____
_____
_____

Exercise Seven:_____

Complete each of the words below with a second syllable. The first syllable is *open*.

1. This was the mo_____ she had dreaded. The exam pa_____s were being given out.
   She be_____ to write quickly. History was her fa_____ subject. She
   ho_____ she would do well.

2. The dri_____ got into his car and started the engine. Luckily, he no_____ the child
   hi_____ behind the van otherwise there might have been a terrible accident.

3. The ba_____ was asleep in the cra_____. His mother ho_____ he would rest now.

4. The girl was ri_____ her horse across the o_____ countryside.

5. The pu_____ had a ru_____, pencil and pa_____. Now he could do his homework.

6. The gro_____ was o_____ on Fri_____ for the sale of eggs, ba_____ and butter.

7. 'Be si_____!' snapped the old la_____. 'I am trying to read.'

8. Today's lo_____ pa_____ announced, 'Team wins a_____ match'. We were all very proud.

As we have seen, when a word has two consonants with one vowel on either side of them, the word is divided between the two letters. This will usually lead to a *short* vowel sound in the first syllable.
Example:

ladder	=	lad / der
common	=	com / mon
compost	=	com / post
contain	=	con / tain
confuse	=	con / fuse

6. However, if you have a word of two syllables with only ONE consonant surrounded by vowels, you have to choose.

Does the one consonant stay with the first syllable, or join the second syllable?
Will the first syllable be *open*, or *closed*? Have a *long* or *short* vowel sound?
The pronunciation of the word will be affected by your decision. To be sure you must say the word aloud. This will help you to decide.
Example:

Do you say	hum an (closed syllable, short *u* sound) or
	hu man (open syllable, long *u* sound)?
Is it	com ic (closed syllable, short *o* sound) or
	co mic (open syllable, long *o* sound)?
Is it	lat er (closed syllable, short *a* sound) or
	la ter (open syllable, long *a* sound)?

Exercise Eight:_____

Say each of the following words aloud and listen carefully to the sound of the first vowel. Try to read each word firstly with a *closed* initial syllable (a *short* vowel), and then with an *open* initial syllable (a *long* vowel sound). When you have decided which is correct, divide the word into two syllables. (If the initial vowel makes a *long* vowel sound, divide the word immediately after the vowel. This will create an *open* initial syllable and the vowel will 'say' its name. If it is a *short* vowel sound you want, divide the word after the consonant following the vowel.) Put in the *stress mark* and mark the initial vowel with a macron or a breve depending upon the sound it makes.

crocus	_____	vowel	_____	frozen	_____
robin	_____	savage	_____	retina	_____
tiny	_____	minus	_____	famine	_____
hoping	_____	plumage	_____	virus	_____
banish	_____	devil	_____	slogan	_____
shadow	_____	spider	_____	damage	_____
modern	_____	carat	_____	tripod	_____

Exercise Nine: _____

Divide these words into syllables. Always divide into syllables between two consonants. Say the word aloud, to help you decide whether to divide after or before a *single* consonant. The first one has been done for you.

consonant	con/son/ant	insolvent	_____	accountant	_____
forgotten	_____	openly	_____	computer	_____
embellish	_____	commitment	_____	excavation	_____
expectation	_____	devotion	_____	demolish	_____
forbidden	_____	exploration	_____	creation	_____
insecure	_____	gymnastic	_____	geology	_____

Exercise Ten: _____

Now it is your turn to create some words. I shall give you two letters with which you must begin two words: one will have an *open* initial syllable, the other a *closed* initial syllable.

Example:

| | | OPEN | CLOSED | |
| | *co* | *co*/hort | *com*/ic | |

de	_____	_____	re	_____	_____
pa	_____	_____	ca	_____	_____
fu	_____	_____	li	_____	_____

pe _____ _____   hu _____ _____

mo _____ _____   di _____ _____

Exercise Eleven: _____

Rearrange these syllables to make a sensible word. Take care that you read an *open* syllable with a *long* vowel sound, and a *closed* syllable with a *short* vowel sound.

ches or tra	_____	phant el e	_____
ter pu com	_____	to mos qui	_____
ber cum cu	_____	la brel um	_____
tic fan tas	_____	or it cred	_____
ore car niv	_____	so dy rhap	_____
chet ric o	_____	lec tric e	_____
cu cal late	_____	tos as bes	_____
sas sin as	_____	gan gi tic	_____
phat em ic	_____	u cate ed	_____
tic e las	_____	lab e ate or	_____

THE *Hard* AND *Soft c* SOUND

The letter *c* can say two sounds: *k* or *s*

At the beginning and in the middle of a word:

1. *c* is hard, as in *cat*, when it is followed by *a, o* or *u*.
Example:

can	medical
cot	acorn
cut	locust

2. *c* has a soft sound, making a *s* sound, when it is followed by *i, e* or *y*.
Example:

city	innocent
centre	bicycle
cygnet	medicine

3. To achieve the hard sound of the letter *c* when it is followed be *e, i* or *y,* use the letter *k.*

Example:

kept	monkey
kidnap	napkin
kick	handkerchief
kerb	broken
ketchup	blanket

Look in a dictionary at the *k* words, and you will see that most of the *k* words begin with *ke, ki* or *kn.* That is because the *k* is either not sounded (*kn*) or a hard *c* sound is needed before *e* or *i.* Words beginning with *ce* or *ci* are pronounced with an *s.*

4. Use *c* for a hard *k* sound when there is no reason to use *k,* that is before *a, o* and *u* or another consonant.

Example:

crisp	carrot
conflict	comic
cliff	curve

At the end of a word:

5. If a ONE syllable word with ONE *short* vowel ends in a *k* sound only, use *ck* never *kk.*

When two consonants follow a vowel, it keeps the vowel *short.* For a word ending in a *k* sound, we must apply the *One, Two, Three Rule.* The letter *k* must be the third letter after the *short* vowel. Count from the first vowel and put in a *c,* or another consonant, to make *k* number three. (See Book One of this Series.)

Example:

123	123
ba*ck*	ba*nk*
de*ck*	si*nk*
si*ck*	pa*rk*
so*ck*	po*rk*
lu*ck*	lu*rk*

6. Use *k* at the end of a word with a *long* vowel sound.

Remember a vowel is always *short* except when you deliberately make it *long.* To make a vowel *long* and so say its *name* we can either place two vowels next to each other (a *vowel digraph*), or use a *silent e.* When the *long* vowel sound is made by placing two vowels together such as *ee, ea,* and *oa,* again, as above, apply the *One, Two, Three Rule* which says that the letter *k* must be the third letter after the first vowel.

Example:

k sound at the end of a word that ends in *silent e*:

cake

brake

hike

k sound at the end of a word that has two vowels in it:

123

leak

meek

soak

At the beginning of a word, the sound of *s* is sometimes written with an *s* and sometimes with a *c*. *C* can only sound *s* before *e*, *i* and *y*. There is no rule to tell us whether to use *s* or *c* before *e*, *i* or *y* and it may be a case of having to rely upon visual memory to help us. Make a special note of any *s* sounding word that presents you with a problem. Look at it frequently to familiarise yourself with it. Learn it.

PRACTICE : THE *Hard* AND S*oft c* SOUND

The letter c can say two sounds: *k* or *s*.
  1. *c* before *a*, *o* and *u* makes a hard *k* sound.
  2. *c* before *e*, *i* or *y* makes a soft *s* sound.

To keep a hard *k* sound at the beginning and in the middle of a word:
  3. **Use *k* for the hard *k* sound before *e*, *i* or *y*.**
  4. **Use *c* for the *k* sound when there is no reason to use *k*, that is, before *a*, *o* and *u* or another consonant.**

At the end of a word:
  5. **Always use *k* for a hard *k* sound at the end of a one syllable word following a short vowel and a consonant.**
  6. **Never use *kk* at the end of a one syllable word ending in only a *k* sound, always use *ck* (see *The 123 Rule*).**
  7. **Use *k* for a hard *k* sound at the end of a long vowel sound with either a *silent e* or a *vowel digraph*.**

Now let us study each of these Rules carefully one at a time.

Firstly, let us concentrate on the *soft c* sound at the beginning, in the middle or at the end of a word.

Exercise Twelve: _____

Soft c words.

Read and copy each of the following *soft c* words saying aloud the letters as you do so. In each case, circle the letter which makes the *c* soft. Study the letter patterns and syllables carefully and when you are ready, cover over the word and try to rewrite it from memory.

Ceylon   _____ _____   fence   _____ _____

centre   _____ _____   distance   _____ _____

cycle	_____ _____	icicle	_____ _____
city	_____ _____	cinder	_____ _____
cigar	_____ _____	Pacific	_____ _____
circus	_____ _____	decide	_____ _____
cygnet	_____ _____	cellar	_____ _____
cement	_____ _____	central	_____ _____
cyclone	_____ _____	certain	_____ _____
cell	_____ _____	citizen	_____ _____
certain	_____ _____	office	_____ _____
cider	_____ _____	notice	_____ _____
pencil	_____ _____	source	_____ _____
voice	_____ _____	mercy	_____ _____
face	_____ _____	recent	_____ _____
silence	_____ _____	fancy	_____ _____
spice	_____ _____	difference	_____ _____
decide	_____ _____	conference	_____ _____
princess	_____ _____	prince	_____ _____
place	_____ _____	cedar	_____ _____
produce	_____ _____	cease	_____ _____
peace	_____ _____	recite	_____ _____

Explain in your own words the Rule you have been applying above.

_____

_____

Now you think of six words with a *soft c* spelling at the beginning, in the middle or at the end of a word. Write them below. Find two words that use an *e*, two that use an *i* and two that use a *y* to make the *c soft*.

_____

_____

Use three of these words in sentences of your own.

_____

_____

_____

Hard *c* words, using *c* and *k*.

Exercise Thirteen:_____

Read and copy each of the following *hard c* words saying aloud the letters as you do so.
In each case, circle the letter that makes the *c hard*. Study the letter patterns and syllables carefully,
and when you are ready, cover over each word and try to rewrite it from memory.

camp	_____	_____	capital	_____	_____
cannon	_____	_____	case	_____	_____
common	_____	_____	clover	_____	_____
curb	_____	_____	coffee	_____	_____
catch	_____	_____	coach	_____	_____
collar	_____	_____	coil	_____	_____
kerb	_____	_____	cube	_____	_____
custom	_____	_____	culprit	_____	_____
kidnap	_____	_____	cure	_____	_____
kick	_____	_____	fraction	_____	_____
conceal	_____	_____	cargo	_____	_____
kettle	_____	_____	clasp	_____	_____
cattle	_____	_____	comb	_____	_____
key	_____	_____	picture	_____	_____
kindle	_____	_____	shrinking	_____	_____
curtain	_____	_____	conflict	_____	_____
caller	_____	_____	detective	_____	_____

Why are some of the *hard c* words spelt with a *c* and some with a *k*? Explain fully the Rules.

_____

_____

Find 6 words of your own beginning with a *hard c* sound: find three spelt with a *c* and three with a *k*.

_____

_____

Use as many of your words as possible in two sentences below.

_____

_____

Exercise Fourteen: _____

Applying the Rules concerning the *soft c* and the *hard k* sound, explain why the following words are spelt as they are:

*k*etchup   _____

*c*entre _____

con*k*er (2 sounds) _____

ac*c*ent (2 sounds) _____

*cy*clone (2 sounds)_____

*c*ir*c*le (2 sounds)   _____

Revision:
1. **c before *a*, *o* and *u* makes a hard *k* sound.**
2. **c before *e*, *i* or *y* makes a soft *s* sound.**
3. **Use *k* for a hard *k* sound before *e*, *i* or *y*.**
4. **Use *c* for a hard *k* sound before another consonant.**

Exercise Fifteen: _____

Insert the missing letter in the following words. Say each word aloud. Listen carefully to the sound of the *c,* and by applying the 4 Rules above, insert *c* or *k*, depending on whether it should be a *hard k* sound or a *soft s* sound. Write the word on the line provided. Then in the brackets at the end of each word write (1) if the first Rule above has been applied, (2) if it is the second Rule, (3) if it is the third Rule, or (4) if the fourth Rule has been applied.

_ipper   _____ (___)   _liff   _____ (___)

_areless   _____ (___)   medi_ine   _____ (___)

_itten   _____ (___)   _attle   _____ (___)

_ertain   _____ (___)   chan_e   _____ (___)

__urtain   _____   (___) __ir__us   _____   (__)(__)

__estrel   _____   (___) __ept   _____   (__)

re__ite   _____   (___) __orridor   _____   (__)

__u__umber_____   (__)(__) __erb   _____   (__)

respe__t   _____   (___) __eeper   _____   (__)

do__tor   _____   (___) s__arlet   _____   (__)

__assette   _____   (___) a__ __ent   _____   (__)(__)

a_ _elerate   _____   (__)(__) __indred   _____   (__)

__artoon   _____   (___) __ir__le   _____   (__)(__)

__ir__ulate   _____   (__)(__) __ir__umstan_e _____   (__)(__)(__)

__ennel   _____   (___) pro__ess   _____   (__)

re__eive   _____   (___) __entenary   _____   (__)

su__ __ess   _____   (__)(__) __riti__ism   _____   (__)(__)

__astle   _____   (___) __ettle   _____   (__)

ex__ited   _____   (___) __etchup   _____   (__)

__a__e   _____   (__)(__) __arve   _____   (__)

Use each of the following words in sentences of your own so that the meaning of each word is clear from the way you have used it. A dictionary may help.

            canter   recite   circulate   centenary

_____

_____

_____

_____

Now let us look at the hard *k* sound at the end of a word.

Revision:

The *ONE, TWO, THREE Rule* states that in a word of ONE syllable with ONE short vowel, the letter *k* must be the third letter when counting from the short vowel. The second letter can be any consonant, but in the case of a *k* sound only at the end of a word, we can never use *kk*, only *ck*. (See Book One of this Series.)

> 1. **Always use *k* for a *hard k* sound at the end of a one syllable word following a short vowel and a consonant.**
> 2. **Never use *kk* at the end of a one syllable word ending in a *k* sound only, always use *ck*.**
> 3. **Always use *k* for a *k* sound after a long vowel which may be formed by placing two vowels together to make one vowel sound (a *vowel digraph*), or by using a *silent e*.**
> 4. **Use *c* for a hard *k* sound when there is no reason to use *k*, that is, before *a*, *o* and *u*, or another consonant.**

Exercise Sixteen: _____

Each gap below says *k*. Insert the missing letter(s) at the end of the following words: use *c*, *k* or *ck*. Write the word carefully on the line provided. In the brackets at the end of the word write (1), (2), (3) or (4) according to which of the four Rules above is being applied.

expe__t	_____	(____)	shrin__ing	_____	(____)
sma__ing	_____	(____)	ris__y	_____	(____)
dete__tive	_____	(____)	strea__	_____	(____)
cri__et	_____	(____)	ban__ing	_____	(____)
ta__le	_____	(____)	kios__	_____	(____)
la__ing	_____	(____)	lea__	_____	(____)
kin__	_____	(____)	tan__er	_____	(____)
cor__s__rew	_____	(__)(__)	boo__ __ase	_____	(__)(__)
chi__en	_____	(____)	confli__t	_____	(____)
spea__er	_____	(____)	instru__tion	_____	(____)
dar__ness	_____	(____)	chun__y	_____	(____)
shipwre__	_____	(____)	lo__et	_____	(____)
ra__e	_____	(____)	fla__e	_____	(____)
sta__e	_____	(____)	wal__ing	_____	(____)
spar__le	_____	(____)	flo__	_____	(____)
awa__en	_____	(____)	appli__ation	_____	(____)

obsta___le   _____ (____)   thin___ing   _____ (____)

refle___tion   _____ (____)   mar___et   _____ (____)

bris___ly   _____ (____)   blea___   _____ (____)

bul___y   _____ (____)   pa___et   _____ (____)

Explain in your own words the Rules that determine the spelling of the following *k* sounds:

*k*ios*k* (2 rules)_____

_____

boo*k*case (2 rules) _____

_____

WORDS ENDING IN *ic* AND *ick*

When does a word end in *ic* and when *ick*?

1. Use *ick* at the end of a one syllable word (in accordance with the *123 Rule*).
Example:

123	123
brick	prick
trick	flick
stick	click

2. Use *ic* at the end of a word that is made up of more than one syllable.
Example:

> frantic
> Atlantic
> magic
> athletic
> terrific

NOTE: When a vowel suffix is added to a word ending in *ic*, it is necessary to add *k* before the vowel suffix in order to maintain the short vowel sound.
Example: mimi*c*ker, picni*c*king, froli*c*ked, pani*c*ky and traffi*c*ker.

3. If the word is a compound word that is really made up of two one-syllable words joined together, use *ick*.
Example:

home + sick	=	homesick
side + kick	=	sidekick
pin + prick	=	pinprick

(This is true also for compound words ending in *eck*, *ack* and *ock*: sund*eck*, rans*ack*, backp*ack*, hollyh*ock*.)

PRACTICE : THE *ic* AND *ick* ENDING

1. Use *ick* at the end of a one syllable word in accordance with the *123 Rule*.
2. Use *ic* at the end of a word that is made up of more than one syllable.
3. Use *ick* at the end of a compound word that is made up of two simple words.

Exercise Seventeen: _____

Put *ic* or *ick* into these words. Then copy each word carefully, saying each letter aloud as you do so. Study the letter patterns and syllables, and when you are ready, cover the word and try to write it from memory. In the brackets at the end of the word write (1), (2) or (3) according to which of the three Rules above is being applied.

frant____ _____ _____ (____)	sli____ _____ _____ (____)
opt____ _____ _____ (____)	sideki____ _____ _____ (____)
l____ _____ _____ (____)	electr____ _____ _____ (____)
pinpri____ _____ _____ (____)	gigant____ _____ _____ (____)
top____ _____ _____ (____)	st____ _____ _____ (____)
traff____ _____ _____ (____)	pan____ _____ _____ (____)
elast____ _____ _____ (____)	tr____ _____ _____ (____)
picn____ _____ _____ (____)	att____ _____ _____ (____)
bri____ _____ _____ (____)	automat____ _____ _____ (____)
publ____ _____ _____ (____)	dramat____ _____ _____ (____)
Atlant____ _____ _____ (____)	homes____ _____ _____ (____)
pr____ _____ _____ (____)	mechan____ _____ _____ (____)
stat____ _____ _____ (____)	cosmet____ _____ _____ (____)
realist____ _____ _____ (____)	civ____ _____ _____ (____)
k____ _____ _____ (____)	cl____ _____ _____ (____)
mus____ _____ _____ (____)	terrif____ _____ _____ (____)

Exercise Eighteen: _____

Complete the following sentences putting *ic* or *ick* into each of the spaces.

1. The art of publ_____ speaking is to st_____ to the top____ and not to pan_____.

2. The sl_____ of tox_____ waste caused the mechan_____ to be s_____.

3. The ship was on automat____ in the Atlant_____ when the crew became frant_____ at the sight of the gigant____ iceberg.

4. The traff____ was chaot____ when the mechan____ dropped the br____s from the elect____ hoist over the motorway.

5. After the mus_____, while reading a mag____ com____, M_____ felt very homes_____.

6. Is it realist____ to visit the Arct____ crossing the Atlant____ with a cub____ metre of plast____?

7. The fanat____ became frant____ when confronted with the drast____ situation.

8. The syrup was th____ and st____y as it oozed between the rust____ br____ and the walking st____.

Exercise Nineteen: _____

Revision of the *soft* and *hard c* sounds.
With reference to the *soft* and *hard c* Rules with which you are already familiar, explain as fully as you can the spelling of the italicised parts of the words below. The number of Rules you need to discuss is indicated in brackets next to each word.

Why are these words spelt:

1. *C*on*c*entr*ic* and not spelt *k*onsentri*ck* (3 rules)?

   _____
   _____
   _____

2. E*cc*entr*ic* and not spelt e*k*sentri*ck* (3 rules)?

   _____
   _____
   _____

3. Ste*ll*a*c*t*ic* and not spelt ste*l*a*k*ti*ck* (3 rules)?

   _____
   _____
   _____

4. E*cliptic* and not spelt e*kliptick* (2 rules)?

_____

_____

Use each of the following words in sentences of your own so that the meaning of each word is clear from the way you have used it. A dictionary may help.

       concentric   eccentric   stellactic   ecliptic

_____

_____

_____

_____

Exercise Twenty: _____

In each of the following questions you must change one letter in the top word to make a new sensible word. By changing a different letter in this new word it is possible to make the bottom word, which is given. Write out the sensible word on the line provided.

1.	RAGE	2.	LIKE	3.	CELL	4.	KICK
	____		____		____		____
	CASE		TAKE		PALL		LACK

5.	LACE	6.	BANK	7.	WICK	8.	BACK
	____		____		____		____
	DICE		PACK		MICE		PACE

THE *ch* SPELLING

When two letters are placed together to represent one sound, a sound that is completely different from either of the two individual letters, we call it a *digraph*. We have so far looked at several *vowel digraphs*: that is, two vowels that stand together for one vowel sound. For example, *ee*, *ai*, *oa* and *ie* are vowel digraphs.

Examples of *digraphs* made up of consonants would be *gh* as in cou*gh*, *sh* as in *sh*ip, *th* as in *th*ick and *ch* as in *ch*ip. All *consonant digraphs* contain an *h*.

A digraph differs from a *blend* in so far as a blend may be made up of two letters but the sound the blend makes comprises a little of each of the two individual letters. *Bl* as in *bl*end, *cr* as in *cr*own, *fl* as in *fl*ing are examples of blends. If the blend comes at the beginning of the word we call it an *initial* consonant blend, if at the end of a word, we call it a *final* consonant blend. *Ng* as in si*ng*, and *nk* as in thi*nk* are final consonant blends. In this section I shall look at the digraph, *ch*.

The English language is very complex. It has many origins.

Ch SAYING *k*

When an English word is of Greek origin, *ch* usually says *k*.

Example:

a*ch*e
*ch*aos
or*ch*estra
*ch*aracter
s*ch*ool
*Ch*rist
*ch*emistry

Exercise Twenty-One:_____

The following words all contain a *k* sound that is spelt *ch*. Put *ch* into these words. Each gap says *k*. When you have finished, copy each word saying aloud each letter as you do so. Study the letter patterns and syllables carefully. When you are ready, cover over each word and try to rewrite it from memory.

___aracter	_____ _____	___asm	_____ _____
___aotic	_____ _____	___loroform	_____ _____
___emical	_____ _____	___emistry	_____ _____
___emist	_____ _____	___lorine	_____ _____
___loroplast	_____ _____	___lorophyll	_____ _____
___aos	_____ _____	___orister	_____ _____
___oral	_____ _____	___oir	_____ _____
___olera	_____ _____	___olesterol	_____ _____
_oreography	_____ _____	___rist	_____ _____
___ristian	_____ _____	___ristmas	_____ _____
___ristopher	_____ _____	___romium	_____ _____
_romosome	_____ _____	___ronic	_____ _____
_ronicle	_____ _____	___rysalis	_____ _____
___orus	_____ _____	___ord	_____ _____

___arisma	_____	_____	a___e	_____	_____
___ronic	_____	_____	___ristine	_____	_____
or___estra	_____	_____	s___eme	_____	_____
s___ool	_____	_____	s___olar	_____	_____
s___olarship	_____	_____	ar___ive	_____	_____
an___or	_____	_____	or___id	_____	_____
e___o	_____	_____	ar___itect	_____	_____
stoma___	_____	_____	te___nical	_____	_____
___olera	_____	_____	me___anic	_____	_____

Exercise Twenty-Two: _____

Use each of the following five words in sentences of your own so that the meaning of each word is clear from the way you have used it. A dictionary may help.

archive   chasm   chlorophyll   chord   chorister

_____
_____
_____
_____
_____

Exercise Twenty-Three: _____

Put into alphabetical order the first 15 words in the first column in Exercise Twenty-One.

_____
_____
_____
_____
_____

Exercise Twenty-Four: _____

Revise the Rules concerning the *hard k* sound. Then complete the sentences below using either *ch, c,* or *k*. All the spaces in the sentences are sounded *hard k*.

1. ____an ____eith ____ome to the ____oir pra____tice at s____ool tonight? We are singing ____ristmas ____arols.

2. I prefer te____ni____al, artisti____ and ____reative subje____ts at s____ool to physi____al ones.

3. ____ristopher ____aused ____aos in the ____emistry lab when he ____ompletely ____overed the Bunsen burner with a ____otton ____loth from the ____itchen.

4. The ____ar me____ani____ likes either ____ustard or ____etchup on his ____ippers!

5. The se____retary to the ____ompany ar____ite____t sent a ____overing letter en____losing an interesting s____eme for ____ontrolling traffi____ ____aos at pea____ times in the city centre. We will ____onsider it at the next ____ouncil ____ommittee meeting.

6. There is an unusual ____ara____ter in the ____emistry lab who is ____omplaining about the smell of ____lorine gas which is ____oming out of the fume ____upboard in the ____orner of the room. He says it is giving him stoma____-a____e and heada____e and is ____eeping him from ____oncentrating.

Exercise Twenty-Five: _____

Put *k*, *ck*, *c* or *ch* into the spaces in the following words. All gaps make a *hard k* sound. Copy each word saying aloud the letters as you do so. Study the letter patterns and syllables, and then when you are ready, cover the word and try to rewrite it from memory.

__ara__ter	_____	_____	__osmeti__	_____	_____
e__o	_____	_____	or__estra	_____	_____
ar__ite__t	_____	_____	traffi__	_____	_____
__on__rete	_____	_____	sil__	_____	_____
_oncentri__	_____	_____	ti__lish	_____	_____
__ristopher	_____	_____	ho__ey	_____	_____
racetra__	_____	_____	dar__en	_____	_____
me__ani__	_____	_____	hunchba__	_____	_____
co__pit	_____	_____	te__ni__al	_____	_____
__oral	_____	_____	stri__t	_____	_____
__aos	_____	_____	__ristmas	_____	_____
spar__le	_____	_____	__arol	_____	_____
heada__e	_____	_____	tan__er	_____	_____

blan__et	_____ _____	bea__er	_____ _____
mar__et	_____ _____	__ord	_____ _____
__romium	_____ _____	__ra__er	_____ _____
mas__	_____ _____	spea__	_____ _____
__ri__et	_____ _____	or__id	_____ _____

Ch SAYING *sh*

When an English word is of French origin, *ch* usually says *sh*.

Example:

*ch*ef

*ch*ampagne

ma*ch*ine

para*ch*ute

Exercise Twenty-Six: _____

Each of these words is of French origin where *ch* says *sh*. Copy each word carefully saying aloud each letter as you write it. Study the letter patterns and the syllables, then when you are ready cover over each word and try to write it from memory.

champagne	_____ _____	chateau	_____ _____
chassis	_____ _____	chef	_____ _____
chalet	_____ _____	chauffeur	_____ _____
chandelier	_____ _____	charade	_____ _____
chivalry	_____ _____	chivalrous	_____ _____
chute	_____ _____	machine	_____ _____
chic	_____ _____	machinery	_____ _____
parachute	_____ _____	brochure	_____ _____
schedule	_____ _____	Cheyenne	_____ _____
chaperone	_____ _____	chauvinist	_____ _____

Exercise Twenty-Seven:_____

Use each of the following five words in sentences of your own so that the meaning of each word is clear from the way you have used it. A dictionary may help.

      chute   brochure   chassis   charade   chaperone

_____

_____

_____

_____

_____

Exercise Twenty-Eight: _____

Put into alphabetical order the first 10 words in the first column in Exercise Twenty-Six.

_____

_____

_____

Exercise Twenty-Nine: _____

Put *sh* or *ch* into the spaces in these words. Each gap says *sh*. There is no guiding rule to help you, only visual memory. Use your eye to judge which looks right.

____oot	para___ute	____alet	____arade
____utter	____ovel	____ambles	bro____ure
____ute	ma____ine	____erry	____awl
____erbet	____ivalry	____ampagne	____andelier
ma____	____immer	____auffeur	____assis

Exercise Thirty:_____

Choose the correct spelling from the words in the brackets. Carefully delete the incorrectly spelt word, so your choice is clear. Use your eye to judge which looks right.

1. The (shauffeur/chauffeur) brought the (Chevrolet/Shevrolet) to the front steps of the (shalet/chalet) so the ladies could (chelter/shelter) from the rain a little longer.

2. It says in the (broshure/brochure) that the French hotel has a (sheff/chef) who serves (mushrooms/muchrooms) in (shampain/champagne) sauce for dinner every day.

3. The mechanic used the (mashine/machine) to lift the body of the car off its (shassie/chassis).

4. The builder of the (shateau/chateau) was so far behind (shedule/schedule) that instead of carrying bricks to the ground, he had to (shoot/chute) them down a (shoot/chute) and hope they did not damage.

Ch OR *tch* AT THE END OF A WORD

When is *ch* and *tch* used at the end of a word?

1. Use *tch* after a *short* vowel sound.
Example:

> d*i*tch
> sw*i*tch
> b*a*tch
> h*u*tch
> m*a*tch

2. Use *ch* after a vowel digraph that gives a *long* vowel sound.
Example:

> pe*a*ch
> be*a*ch
> co*a*ch
> scre*e*ch

3. Use *ch* after a vowel plus a consonant (other than *t*).
Example:

> pe*r*ch
> to*r*ch
> pu*n*ch
> chu*r*ch
> la*r*ch
> be*n*ch

Important exceptions to note: which?(but witch), such, rich, much.
These are all *exceptions* because each time *ch* instead of *tch* follows a short vowel sound (Rule 1 above).

PRACTICE : THE *ch* OR *tch* ENDING

> **1. Use *tch* after a short vowel sound.**
> **2. Use *ch* after a vowel digraph that gives a long vowel sound.**
> **3. Use *ch* after a vowel plus a consonant (other than *t*).**

Exercise Thirty-One: _____

Place *ch* or *tch* into the following words. Each space says *ch* as in *chip*. Copy each word, saying aloud the letters as you do so. When you are ready, cover over each word and try to write it from memory.

coa____	_____	_____	di____	_____	_____
wi____	_____	_____	ma____	_____	_____
whi____?	_____	_____	scree____	_____	_____
per____	_____	_____	rea____	_____	_____
hu____	_____	_____	bun____	_____	_____
chur____	_____	_____	wa____	_____	_____
pea____	_____	_____	sna____	_____	_____
i____	_____	_____	pa____	_____	_____
star____	_____	_____	pun____	_____	_____
sti____	_____	_____	pi____fork	_____	_____
tor____	_____	_____	cockroa____	_____	_____
por____	_____	_____	pi____	_____	_____
bir____	_____	_____	crun____	_____	_____
Du____	_____	_____	clu____	_____	_____
Sco____	_____	_____	stre____	_____	_____
tren____	_____	_____	fe____	_____	_____
ran____	_____	_____	lun____	_____	_____
dren____	_____	_____	ki____en	_____	_____
poa____	_____	_____	hi____hiker	_____	_____
tea____	_____	_____	scor____	_____	_____
ba____	_____	_____	stre____er	_____	_____
sa____el	_____	_____	scra____	_____	_____
crou____	_____	_____	bran____	_____	_____
swi____	_____	_____	tou____	_____	_____

Exercise Thirty-Two: _____

Each of the following words has more that one meaning. Use each word twice - in two sentences - so that the 2 meanings of the word are clear from the way each is used. A dictionary will help.

      pitch   clutch   match   poach

_____
_____
_____
_____

What is a *latch*?

_____
_____

What is meant by the *reach* of a river?

_____

To which group of food does *starch* belong?

_____

What does the word *pitch* mean in *pitch*fork? What is a *pitchfork* used for?

_____
_____

THE SOFT *g* SOUND

> **In exactly the same way as *c* followed by *e, i* or *y* says
> a *soft c* or *s* sound, *g* followed by *e, i* or *y* says a *soft g* or *j* sound.**

Example:
At the beginning of a word:

    gentle
    gypsy
    gyroscope
    giant

In the middle or at the end of a word:

    large
    village
    energy
    magic
    Egypt

Exercise Thirty-Three: _____

Each of these words makes a *soft g* or *j* sound. Copy each word carefully saying aloud each letter as you do so. Study the letter patterns and syllables and when you are ready cover over each word and try to rewrite it from memory.

g followed by an *e*:

genuine	_____	_____	gesture	_____	_____
genius	_____	_____	germination	_____	_____
general	_____	_____	geology	_____	_____
geometry	_____	_____	geography	_____	_____
generous	_____	_____	Georgian	_____	_____
gentle	_____	_____	gelatine	_____	_____

g followed by an *i*:

gist	_____	_____	gigantic	_____	_____
ginger	_____	_____	gipsy	_____	_____
giraffe	_____	_____	giro	_____	_____

g followed by a *y*:

gymnast	_____	_____	gyrate	_____	_____
gymnasium	_____	_____	gyroscope	_____	_____
gymkhana	_____	_____	gypsum	_____	_____

soft g in the middle or at the end of a word:

pigeon	_____	_____	large	_____	_____
angel	_____	_____	orange	_____	_____
agent	_____	_____	syringe	_____	_____
digestion	_____	_____	marriage	_____	_____
danger	_____	_____	revenge	_____	_____
stranger	_____	_____	imagine	_____	_____
energy	_____	_____	religion	_____	_____

damage	_____	_____	huge	_____	_____
village	_____	_____	privilege	_____	_____
magic	_____	_____	sergeant*	_____	_____
change	_____	_____	tragedy	_____	_____
charge	_____	_____	vegetable	_____	_____

*Explain in your own words why there is an *e* following the *g* in ser*ge*ant. Explain why it is not sounded - that the *ea* in this case is not a vowel digraph that should be pronounced *ee*.

_____

_____

Can you think of 3 more words that follow this pattern - for the same reason? List them below.

_____

Exercise Thirty-Four: _____

Put into alphabetical order the first 12 words in the first column in Exercise Thirty-Three.

_____

_____

_____

_____

_____

Exercise Thirty-Five: _____

Use each of the following five words in sentences of your own so that the meaning of each word is clear from the way you have used it. A dictionary may help.

    gyroscope   gypsum   germination   gist   gymkhana

_____

_____

_____

_____

_____

_G_ and _c_ followed by _e, i_ or _y_ give their _soft_ sounds: _c_ says _s_ and _g_ says _j_. When the suffixes _able_ and _ous_ are added to a word ending with a soft _c_ or _g_ sound, the _silent e_ at the end of the word must remain, or be changed to an _i_, otherwise the _a_ in _able_ or the _o_ in _ous_ will have the effect of making the _c_ and _g_ hard.

Example:

$$courage + ous = courag\textit{e}ous$$
$$knowledge + able = knowledg\textit{e}able$$
$$trace + able = trac\textit{e}able$$

Exercise Thirty-Six:_____

Compete these *word sums.* In all these words, the *e* remains. The first one has been done for you.

manage + able	_____manageable_____	outrage + ous	_____
change + able	_____	notice + able	_____
service + able	_____	advantage + ous	_____
pronounce + able	_____	service + able	_____
replace + able	_____	knowledge + able	_____
charge + able	_____	courage + ous	_____

Exercise Thirty-Seven: _____

Unjumble these letters to make sensible *soft g* sounding words that have something to do with these clues.

(tengle) Not harsh, soft	_____	(ronega) A fruit	_____
(guhe) Enormous	_____	(giepno) A bird	_____
(uniseg) Very clever	_____	(merg) A microbe	_____
(itnag) A large person	_____	(rygnee) Vigour	_____
(livlgea) Not a town	_____	(gcuraoe) Bravery	_____

THE *j* SOUND

The *ge* and *dge* Endings.

> **No English word ends in *j*. At the end of a one-syllable
> word the *j* sound is spelt *ge* or *dge*.**

When is *ge* used, and when is *dge* used?

1. *dge* (a long ending) always follows a *short* vowel sound.
Example:

fudge
ledge

bridge

lodge

Remember when two consonants follow a vowel they have the effect of 'protecting' the vowel from the influence of another vowel which may follow it. In this way, the first vowel retains its *short* sound. In each of the words above, the two vowels are 'kept apart' by the two consonants, *d* and *g*. In these words the vowel sound is *short*.

2. *ge* (a short ending) follows a *long* vowel sound.
Example:

stage

huge

wage

page

Here, the *e* of *ge* has two functions: it makes *g* say *j* and it acts as a *silent e* affecting the sound of the vowel. Now the vowel is *long* and so says its *name*.

3. A vowel followed by a consonant takes *ge*.
Example:

large

charge

fringe

plunge

The explanation for this is the same as for Rule One above. Instead of the *d* in *dge* being one of the two consonants 'protecting' the first (short) vowel, there is a consonant already in the word that will do the job of the *d* in *dge*. Hence it is only necessary to add *ge* to this first consonant to achieve two consonants.

PRACTICE : THE *j* SOUND

ge and *dge* both say *j*.

1. **Use *dge* after a *short* vowel sound.**
2. **Use *ge* after a *long* vowel sound.**
3. **A vowel followed by a consonant takes *ge*.**

Exercise Thirty-Eight: _____

Put *ge* or *dge* into each of these words to give a *j* sound at the end of the word. (Look for a *long* or a *short* vowel to help you decide which to use.) Then copy each word carefully saying each letter aloud

as you do so. When you have finished, study the letter patterns in each of the words. Cover over each
word and try to rewrite it from memory.

ju____ _____ _____   ra____ _____ _____

sta____ _____ _____   do____ _____ _____

le____ _____ _____   e____ _____ _____

mi____ _____ _____   lar____ _____ _____

bul____ _____ _____   fri____ _____ _____

we____ _____ _____   hu____ _____ _____

char____ _____ _____   plun____ _____ _____

pa____ _____ _____   bar____ _____ _____

he____ _____ _____   smu____ _____ _____

Explain in your own words when to use:
ge at the end of a word to say *j*:

_____
_____

dge at the end of the word to say *j*:

_____
_____

THE *age* AND *idge* SPELLING

4. It can be seen from the Exercises above that **a *dge* ending is usually found at
the end of a one-syllable word.**
Example:

ri*dge*
bri*dge*
le*dge*

However, these words, which are made up of more than one syllable, also take a *dge*
ending. These *exceptions* to the Rule, are worth learning: knowledge, cartridge,
partridge, porridge.

**5. Otherwise an *idge* sound at the end of a word that is made up of more
than one syllable, is usually spelt *age*.**
Example:

man*age*
post*age*
ramp*age*

mess*age*

Exceptions include: privilege, college.

---

4. *idge* is usually found at the end of a word of one syllable.
5. Use *age* to say *idge* at the end of a word made up of more than one syllable.

Exercise Thirty-Nine:_____

The endings of all these words say *idge*. Choose *idge* or *age* to complete the word and then copy it onto the line provided. Remember the ending of a one syllable word will be spelt *idge*. The *idge* sound at the end of almost all other words will be spelt *age*. Take care! Some of the above exceptions are included in this Exercise.

mi_____ _____   r_____ _____

vill_____ _____   dam_____ _____

post_____ _____   marri___ _____

cartr_____ _____ fr_____ _____

encour___ _____   partr_____ _____

cabb_____ _____   man_____ _____

short_____ _____ langu_____ _____

cribb_____ _____ saus_____ _____

mess_____ _____   le_____ _____

br_____ _____   lugg_____ _____

Exercise Forty: _____

Complete the following sentences putting *age*, *ge* or *dge* into the spaces at the end of the words.

1. At the vill_____ craft fair, the lady selling fu_____ was wearing a lar_____ ba_____ with a flower on it.

2. There was a hu_____ smu_____ of black ink on the e_____ of a pa_____ in my exercise book.

3. There was a short_____ of post_____ stamps at the Post Office so I could not send a mess_____ to my aunt who lives on the e_____ of town.

© 1994 Susan J. Daughtrey M.Ed.

4. If you man_____ to find my lugg _____, please check it is not dam_____d.

5. Don't ju_____ the lar_____ stran_____r too harshly!

6. We use *j* to say *j* when it is followed by *a, o* or *u*.
Example:

> jacket
> January
> judge
> jostle
> jolly

7. We use *j* in the middle or at the end of a word to say *ject*.
Example:

> project
> subject
> objective

---

6. Use *j* to say *j* before *a, o* or *u*.
7. Use *j* in the middle or at the end of a word to say *ject*.

Exercise Forty-One: _____

Use *ge, dge, age, j*, or *g* to say *j* in these words. Copy each word saying aloud each letter as you do so.

____u____ _____   re___ect _____   ____entle _____

villa____ _____   ___oyous _____   ____apan _____

knowle___ _____   saus____ _____   ____ipsy _____

bri____ _____   in__ection _____   ___ymnast _____

____olly _____   we_____ _____   stran___er _____

mana___er _____   sub___ect _____   ____acket _____

ob__ection _____   colle____ _____   gru_____ _____

____ury _____   pro___ect _____   __ostle _____

Explain in your own words why:
jolly, Japan, jury and *jostle* are spelt with a *j*:

_____

_____

gentle, *ginger* and *gymnast* are spelt with a *g*:

_____

_____

g followed by *e*, *i* or *y* says *j*.
j followed by *a*, *o* or *u* says *j*.

Exercise Forty-Two: _____

Using these Rules, fill in *g* or *j* at the beginning of these words. Each space says *j*. Copy carefully
each word, saying aloud each letter as you do so.

___udge	_____	___entle	_____
___ump	_____	___ipsy	_____
___ymnast	_____	___em	_____
___ackdaw	_____	___anuary	_____
___enerator	_____	___eranium	_____
___enuine	_____	___avelin	_____
___ockey	_____	___amboree	_____
___iant	_____	___eneration	_____
___ollity	_____	___ostle	_____
___iraffe	_____	___ovial	_____
___ymkhana	_____	___oyous	_____
___umble	_____	___inger	_____
___unction	_____	___ubilant	_____
___igantic	_____	___ymnastic	_____
___ustify	_____	___ungle	_____
___uvenile	_____	___esture	_____
___yroscope	_____	___ustice	_____

Exceptions. Make a note of these words that begin with *j* even though they are
followed by an *e*:
jet   jelly   Jew   jeans   jealous   jewel   Jerusalem   Jesus   Jersey   jerk

Can you find four more words that begin with *je* for the *j* sound?

_____ _____
_____

8. When the sound *j* is followed by a *long u* sound in the middle of a word, spell it with a *d*.
Example:

 e*d*ucation
gra*d*ual
indivi*d*ual
pen*d*ulum
deci*d*uous

---

8. In the middle of a word, *d* in front of a long *u* says *j* (correctly pronounced *du*).

Exercise Forty-Three:_____

Using all the *j* sound Rules, fill in the following spaces with *j, g, ge, dge* or *d*. Each space says *j*. Copy each word, saying aloud each letter as you do so. Study the letter patterns and syllables carefully. When you are ready, cover over each word and try to write it from memory. Take care! (Note the *s.)

in___ection	_____ _____	___amboree	_____ _____
in___enious	_____ _____	indivi__ual	_____ _____
ob___ection	_____ _____	___u___ment	_____ _____
challen___	_____ _____	advanta___ous*	_____ _____
begru___	_____ _____	pen___ulum	_____ _____
deci___uous	_____ _____	encoura__ment*	_____ _____
knowle___able*	_____ _____	___uvenile	_____ _____
ori___inal	_____ _____	pro___ection	_____ _____
colle___	_____ _____	e__ucation	_____ _____
___igantic	_____ _____	cartri___	_____ _____
stran___er	_____ _____	gra__ually	_____ _____
ve___tation	_____ _____	dan___erous	_____ _____

THE *HARD g* SOUND

When *g* is followed by *a, o* or *u* it has a *hard* sound.

Example:

> garden
> gulp
> goddess

KEEPING A *HARD g* SOUND

Often we want to make a hard *g* sound as in *garden,* even though the *g* may be followed by *e, i* or *y*. In these cases:

It is necessary to protect the *g* from the effect of the *e, i* or *y* that follows, by putting a *u* immediately after the *g*.

This acts as a 'wall' and prevents the *e, i* or *y* making the *g soft*. The *u* is not sounded. It is simply doing a job.

Example:

> g*u*est
> g*u*ide
> g*u*y
> vag*u*e
> tong*u*e

Exercise Forty-Four: _____

SOME of these words are deliberately misspelt. Say each word aloud and place a *u*, as in vag*u*e, where you think one is needed. Remember, a *g* followed by *u* makes a *hard g* sound. The influence of the *e, i* or *y* is taken away (blocked). Rewrite each word correctly on the line provided. Mark the Exercises, study the words and, when you are ready, cover over each word and write it from memory.

jagged	_____	_____	gitar	_____	_____
jentle	_____	_____	ginea-pig	_____	_____
fatige	_____	_____	gulp	_____	_____
cataloge	_____	_____	gy	_____	_____
general	_____	_____	jolly	_____	_____
gide	_____	_____	gipsy	_____	_____

giant	_____ _____	jerm	_____ _____
gess	_____ _____	roge	_____ _____
gust	_____ _____	jesture	_____ _____
Roger	_____ _____	gilty	_____ _____
voge	_____ _____	intrige	_____ _____
jovial	_____ _____	arranje	_____ _____
jiraffe	_____ _____	leage	_____ _____
tongue	_____ _____	lodje	_____ _____
gillotine	_____ _____	vage	_____ _____

Exercise Forty-Five: _____

Use each of the following four words in sentences of your own so that the meaning of each word is clear from the way you have used it. A dictionary may help.

rogue   vague   vogue   league

_____
_____
_____
_____

Exercise Forty-Six:_____

Each of the following words has a *hard g* spelling using *u* as a 'wall'. Place one of these words into each set of brackets in the following sentences to replace the words in italics. Use a dictionary to check your answers.

guessed   fatigue   guest   intrigue   dialogue
vogue   vague   catalogue   league   guile

1. The dishonest athlete had used all her *cunning and deceit* (_____) to cheat her opponent out of the trophy.

2. The two actors had a long *conversation* (_____) in Act One.

3. The mountaineers said they were almost forced to give up because of *tiredness* (_____).

4. The toy shop published a *list of toys for sale* (_____) in November.

5. The King discovered the *plot to kill him* (_____) and ordered his soldiers to arrest Guy Fawkes.

6. Miniskirts are not *in fashion* (_____) this year.

7. The memory of his first home was *not very clear* (_____).

8. The *group of people who share an interest* in the local hospital, called the (_____) of Friends, had organised many fund-raising events.

9. In the exam, the student *said what he thought without really knowing* (_____) the answer.

10. The *visitor staying in the hotel* (_____) was asked to sign the Visitors Book.

RULE SUMMARIES

Here you are asked to do three things:
1. Read through all the Rules that have been identified in this book, one at a time.
2. When you are ready, fill in the missing words in the Rule Summaries below.
3. Explain in your own words what is meant by each Rule, making references to the examples given.

SYLLABLES

Read though all the Rules concerning **SYLLABLES** on pages 1 to 8. When you are ready, complete the following Rule Summary without referring to that section.

A syllable is a small part of a word that is pronounced as a unit. Every syllable makes one vowel sound. This may be a single _____ or a vowel _____. The letter ___ is often considered a vowel, but a silent ___ is often discounted because it is doing a job rather than making a _____ sound of its own.

To break up a word into syllables:

1. If there is a double letter in a word, you should divide between the ____ _____. When a word has two _____ with one _____ on each side of them, the word is divided between the two _____.

2. In the same way, we can split any two-syllable word which has two different _____ in the middle and a _____ on either side of them.

3. A _____ mark is a small mark which is used to show emphasis. It is placed at the end of the _____ _____ syllable. Usually the first syllable of an English word is stressed unless the word begins with a _____.

4. If a syllable ends in a _____ it is referred to as a CLOSED SYLLABLE and the vowel sound is _____. It is '____ ____' by the_____.

5. An _____ syllable ends in a _____and the vowel sound is_____.

6. If a word of two syllables has only ONE _____ surrounded by vowels, you have to choose. Saying the word aloud will help. The _____ of the word will be affected by your decision.

Now turn back to pages 1 to 6 and check your answers.

KEEPING YOUR OWN RECORD OF THE SPELLING RULES IN THESE BOOKS

To keep a permanent record of the Spelling Rules in these books - a record to which you can refer at any time - you need a pack of 5ins x 8ins index cards and an index card box or A5 file. You have already made 12 Record Cards from Book One. Continue here with Card Thirteen.

CARD THIRTEEN:

Once you have corrected the Rule Summary concerning **SYLLABLES** above, copy it carefully and clearly onto the first side of Card Thirteen.

On the reverse side of Card Thirteen explain in your own words how an understanding of syllables will help you with your spelling. Include in your explanation the following examples which illustrate all the points you should mention.
Example:

shut/ter   an example of a CLOSED syllable. (Explain.)

ban/ker   (Where do you divide a word which looks like this?)
sub/ject

si/lent
slo/gan   examples of OPEN syllables. (Explain.)
lo/tion

rob/in   saying the word aloud will help with your
vi/rus   decision. How?

CARD FOURTEEN:

Read the Rules concerning **THE *Hard* AND *Soft* c SOUND** on pages 8 to 10. When you are ready, complete the following Rule Summary without referring to that section.

The letter *c* can say two sounds: ___ or ___.
1. *C* makes a *hard* sound when it is followed by ___, ___ and ___.
2. *C* makes a *soft* ___ sound when it is followed by ___, ___ and ___.
3. To keep a *hard k* sound at the beginning and in the middle of the word, use ___ before ___, ___ and ___.
4. Otherwise use ___ for the *k* sound when there is no reason to use ___: that is before ___, ___ and ___ or another consonant.
5. At the end of a one syllable word with one short vowel followed by a consonant, use ___. This is in accordance with the _____ *RULE*.
6. Never use _____ at the end of a one syllable word with one short vowel ending in a *k* sound. Only ever use _____.
7. Use ___ for a *hard* ___ sound following a _____ vowel sound.

Turn back to page 10 and check your answers.

Onto the first side of Card Fourteen copy the ***Hard* AND *Soft* c SOUND** Rules on page 10.

On the reverse side of Card Fourteen:
1. List examples of each part of the Rule. Explain how the examples illustrate each part of the Rule.
2. List as many words as you can which demonstrate in one word the *hard* and the *soft* c sound, such as *conc*entrate, *conk*er.

CARD FIFTEEN:

Read the notes concerning **WORDS ENDING IN *ic* AND *ick*** on page 16 to 17. When you are ready complete the following Rule Summary without referring to that section.

1. Use _____ at the end of a one syllable word (in accordance with the _____**RULE**).
2. Use _____ at the end of a word made up of more than one syllable.
3. Use _____ at the end of a _____ word made up of two _____ words.

Check your answers by referring to page 17 and copy these Rules onto the first side of Card Fifteen.

On the reverse of Card Fifteen explain this Rule in your own words giving Examples to illustrate your answer.

CARD SIXTEEN:
Read the Rules regarding the different sounds **THE *ch* SPELLING** makes on pages 19 to 23.
When you are ready complete the following Rule Summary without referring to those pages.

1. When an English word is of Greek origin, *ch* usually says _____.
2. When an English word is of French origin, *ch* usually says _____.

Check your answers by referring to pages 20 and 23, then copy these two Rules neatly onto the first side
of Card Sixteen giving examples to illustrate the different sounds of **THE *ch* SPELLING**.

On the reverse side of Card Sixteen make a note of the 'usual' sound a *ch* spelling makes. Explain what
is meant by a *digraph,* giving examples to highlight your explanation (mention also a *vowel digraph*),
and explain in what way a *digraph* differs from a *blend* (give examples).

CARD SEVENTEEN:
Read the Rules concerning ***Ch* OR *tch* AT THE END OF A WORD** on page 25 and when you are
ready complete the following Rule Summary without referring to that section.

1. Use ____ after a short vowel sound.
2. Use ___ after a vowel _____ which gives a long vowel sound.
3. Use ___ after a vowel plus a consonant (other than ___).

Read through the Rules on page 25 and check your answers. Copy these Rules onto the first side
of Card Seventeen.

On the reverse side explain these Rules, enriching your explanation with many examples. Make a note
of any *exceptions* to these Rules.

CARD EIGHTEEN:
Read through the notes regarding **THE *SOFT g* SOUND** on pages 27 and 29 and when you are ready
complete the following Rule Summary without referring to those pages.

In the same way as *c* followed by ___, ___ and ___ says a *soft* ___ or ___ sound, so a *g*
followed by ___, ___ and ___ says a *soft* ___ or ___ sound.
When a suffix beginning with *a*, such as _____, or *o*, such as _____ are added to a
word ending in a soft *c* or *g* sound, the *silent e* must NOT be _____ otherwise the
a or the *o* would have the effect of making the ___ and ___ _____.

Check your answers by referring to pages 27 and 29. Copy onto the first side of Card Eighteen the above
Rules.

On the reverse side of Card Eighteen and with reference to the word sums on page 30, explain why it is
necessary to keep the *silent e* when adding a suffix beginning with *a* or *o*. Give examples to
illustrate your answer.

CARD NINETEEN:
Read all the notes about **THE *j* SOUND** on pages 30 to 36 and when you are ready complete the
following Rule Summary.

____ and ____ both say *j*.

1. Use _____ at the end of a word following a *short* vowel.
2. Use ____ after a *long* vowel sound.
3. Use ____ at the end of a word with a vowel plus a _____.
4. _____ is usually found at the end of a word of one syllable.
5. At the end of a word of more than one syllable, use _____ to say *idge*.
6. Use ___ to say *j* after ___, ___ and ___.
7. Use *j* in the middle or at the end of a word to say _____.
8. In the middle of a word ____ before a long *u* sound says *j*, (correctly pronounced ___).

Read pages 30 to 36 to check your answers, then neatly copy these Rules onto the first side of Card Nineteen.

On the reverse of this Card:
a. List any *exceptions* to each part of the Rule and in your own words say why the words are exceptions.
b. Use these examples to help explain why *jolly* is spelt with a *j*, *gentle* with a *g*, *village* with *age*, *bridge* with *idge*, *subject* is spelt with a *j* and *education* with *du* to say *j*.

CARD TWENTY:
Read page 37 about **THE *HARD* g SOUND** and about **KEEPING A *HARD* g SOUND**. When you are ready, complete the following Rule Summary without referring to those sections.

1. When *g* is followed by ___, ___ or ___ it has a *hard* sound as in _____.
2. When *g* is followed by ___, ___ and ___ it has a *soft g* sound as in _____.
3. To protect the *g* from the effect of an ___, ___ or ___ (which would give a *soft g* sound), follow the *g* with a ___. This act as a '_____' and prevents the ___, ___ and ___ having an effect upon the *g* and making the *g soft*. The ___ is not sounded, it is simply doing a job.

Read page 37 to check your answers. Then copy these two Rules onto the first side of Card Twenty.

On the reverse of Card Twenty explain in your own words the third point above, what the *u* is doing and when and why it is necessary. Give lots of examples to illustrate the points you are making.

CARD TWENTY-ONE:
Make a note of any of the words in Book Two which you have found difficult to remember and which you need to look at again. Alongside each word make a note of the Rule to which it belongs, and a page reference, so you can look it up and read over the Rule again. Try to learn these words. Set your Card out like this:

Words I have found difficult to remember in Book Two which I need to look at again:

WORD	RULE	PAGE	LEARNT

ANSWERS

Working *down* the Exercises, the Answers are as follows:

Exercise 1

word	
shut ter	2
sit ter	2
lit ter	4
ken nel	2
quar rel	4
wal low	3

Exercise 2

bot tom
bar ren
dap per
sum mer
wil low
bet ter
sor' row
trac' tor
in vade'
gar den
chim ney
hand bag
big ger
set tee
cot ton
ex pect'
for get'
con cern'

Exercise 3

con cert
ad dress'
crim' son
con fess'
ham' ster
com pose'
ten' nis
in spect'

Exercise 4

gar den
hun closed
mo open
ad closed
spi open
ban' ish
shad' ow
can closed
sub closed
por closed

(Exercise 5 / 6 — open and closed syllables)

ship' ment
han closed
win closed
mi' nus
plu' mage
cra open
dev' li
spi der
car' at
scrib closed
spar closed
fol closed
ret' in a
fam' ine
vi' rus
slo' gan
dam' age
tri' pod
sav' age

Exercise 6

in closed
sta open
sis closed
pro open
sec closed
trans closed
mad closed
hu open
sin closed
lo open
car closed
con closed
re open
fa open
stu open
ca open
com closed

Exercise 7

1. moment papers
2. driver noticed hiding
3. baby cradle hoped
4. riding open
5. pupil ruler paper
6. grocer open Friday
7. silent lady
8. local paper away
   bacon
   began favourite hoped

Exercise 8

cro' cus
rob' in
gym nas tic
ac coun tant
com pu ter
ex cav a tion
de mol ish
cre a tion
ge ol ogy
de vo tion
ex plor a tion
ti' ny
ho' ping
com mit ment
o pen ly
in sol vent

Exercise 9

for got ten
em bell ish
ex pec ta tion
for bid den
in se cure

Exercise 11

orchestra
computer
cucumber
fantastic
carnivore
ricochet
calculate
assassin
emphatic
elastic
elephant
mosquito
umbrella
creditor
rhapsody
electric
asbestos
gigantic
educate
elaborate

Exercise 14

1. *k* before *e* says *k*
2. *c* before *e* says *s*
3. *c* before *o* says *k*
4. *c* before *c* says *k*
   k before *e* says *k*
   c before *e* says *s*
5. *c* before *y* says *s*
   c before *e* says *s*
   c before *y* says *k*
6. *c* before *i* says *s*
   c before *l* says *k*

Exercise 15

word	
kipper	3
careless	1
circumstance	2 1 2
process	2
kitten	3
certain	2
centenary	2
criticism	4 2
curtain	1
kestrel	3
recite	2
cucumber	1 1
carve	1
circle	2 4
kindred	3
accent	4 2
scarlet	1
cliff	4
medicine	2
cattle	1
chance	2
circus	2 1
kept	3
corridor	1
kerb	3
keeper	3
cassette	1
doctor	4
respect	4
cucumber	1 1
recite	2
kettle	3
ketchup	3

Exercise 16

word	
expect	4
smacking	2
detective	4
cricket	2
tackle	2
lacking	2
kink	1
corkscrew	1 4
chicken	2
speaker	3 and *123 Rule*
darkness	1
shipwreck	2
rake	3
stake	3
sparkle	1
awaken	3
obstacle	4
reflection	4
briskly	1

c before *l* says *k*

bulky 1
shrinking 1
risky 1
streak 3
banking 1
kiosk 1
leak 3
tanker 1
bookcase 1 4
conflict 4
instruction 4
chunky 1
locket 2
flake 3
walking 1
flock 2
application 4
thinking 1
market 1
bleak 3
packet 2

k before *i* says *k*
osk = *123 Rule*
ook = *123 Rule*
c before *a* says *k*

Exercise 17
frantic 2
optic 2
lick 1
pinprick 3
topic 2
traffic 2
elastic 2
picnic 2
brick 1
public 2

Atlantic 2
prick 1
static 2
realistic 2
kick 1
music 2
slick 1
sidekick 3
electric 2
gigantic 2
stick 1
panic 2
trick 1
attic 2
automatic 2
dramatic 2
homesick 3
mechanic 2
cosmetic 2
civic 2
click 1
terrific 2

Exercise 18
1. public stick topic panic
2. slick toxic mechanic sick
3. automatic Atlantic frantic gigantic
4. traffic chaotic mechanic bricks electric
5. music magic comic Mick homesick
6. realistic Arctic Atlantic cubic plastic

7. fanatic frantic drastic
8. thick sticky rustic brick stick

Exercise 19
1. *c* before *o* says *k*
   c before *e* says *s*
   ends *ic* - more than one syllable
2. *c* before *c* says *k*
   c before *e* says *s*
   ends *ic* - more than one syllable
3. *ll* after *e* *123 Rule*
   c before *t* says *k*
   ends *ic* - more than one syllable
4. *c* before *l* says *k*
   ends *ic* - more than one syllable

Exercise 20
1. CAGE
2. LAKE
3. CALL
4. LICK
5. LICE
6. BACK
7. MICK
8. PACK

Exercise 23
chaos
chaotic
character
charisma
chemical

chemist
chloroplast
cholera
choral
choreography
chorus
Christian
Christopher
chromosome
chronicle

Exercise 24
1. Can Keith come choir
   practice school
   Christmas carols
2. technical artistic
   creative subjects
   school physical
3. Christopher caused
   chaos chemistry
   completely covered
   cotton cloth kitchen
4. car mechanic
   custard ketchup
   kippers
5. secretary company
   architect covering
   enclosing scheme
   controlling traffic
   chaos peak consider
   council committee
6. character chemistry
   complaining chlorine
   coming cupboard
   corner stomach
   ache headache
   keeping concentrating orchid

Exercise 25
character
echo
architect
concrete
concentric
Christopher
racetrack
mechanic
cockpit
choral
chaos

sparkle
headache
blanket
market
chromium
mask
cricket
cosmetic
orchestra
traffic
silk
ticklish
hockey
darken
hunchback
technical
strict
Christmas
carol
tanker
beaker
chord
cracker
speak

Exercise 28
chalet
champagne
chandelier
chaperone
chassis
chic
chivalry
chute
parachute
schedule

Exercise 29
shoot
shutter
chute
sherbet
mash
parachute
shovel
machine
chivalry
shimmer
chalet
shambles
sherry
champagne
chauffeur
charade
brochure
shawl
chandelier
chassis

Exercise 30
1. chauffeur
   Chevrolet
   chalet shelter
2. brochure chef
   mushrooms
   champagne
3. machine chassis
4. chateau schedule
   shoot chute

Exercise 31
coach
witch
which?
perch
hutch
church
peach
itch
starch
stitch
torch
porch
birch
Dutch
Scotch
trench
ranch
drench
poach
teach
batch
satchel
crouch
switch
ditch

match
screech
reach
bunch
watch
snatch
patch
punch
pitchfork
cockroach
pitch
crunch
clutch
stretch
fetch
lunch
kitchen
hitchhiker
scorch
stretcher
scratch
branch
touch

Exercise 33
serge ant - *g* before *e*
says *j* (*soft g*). If no *e*,
ga would say *g* (*hard g*

Exercise 35
general
generous
genius
gentle
genuine
geometry
ginger

giraffe
gist
gymkhana
gymnasium
gymnast

Exercise 37
gentle
huge
genius
message
bridge
village
giant
orange
pigeon
germ
fridge
partridge
manage
language
courage
energy

Exercise 38
sausage
ledge
stage
judge
ledge
luggage
grudge
jacket
stranger
jungle
gesture
justice
gymnastic
jostle
midge
bulge
wedge
charge
page
hedge
rage
dodge
dodge
edge
large
edge
huge
fridge
large
plunge
barge
smudge

Exercise 39
midge
village
postage
cartridge
encourage
cabbage
shortage
cribbage
message
bridge
ridge
damage
marriage
gentle
Japan
ginger
joyous
jovial
jubilant
subject
college
project
wedge
injection
sausage
geranium
javelin
jamboree
generation
gem
January
gipsy or gypsy
reject
joyous
gentle
objection
gyroscope
juvenile
jolly
manager
jury
justify
juvenile
gipsy or gypsy

Exercise 40
1. village fudge
large badge
2. huge smudge
edge page
3. shortage postage
message edge
4. manage luggage
damaged
5. judge large stranger

Exercise 41
judge
village
knowledge
jumble
junction
gigantic
giraffe
gymkhana
jamboree
individual
judgement

Exercise 42
judge
jump
gymnast
jackdaw
generator
genuine
jockey
jollity
giraffe
gigantic

Exercise 43
injection
ingenious
objection
challenge
begrudge
deciduous
knowledgeable
original
college
gigantic
stranger
vegetation
germ
gipsy or gypsy
jolly
guy
gulp
guinea-pig
guitar
guillotine
tongue
giraffe
jovial
vogue
Roger
gust
guess
guide
general
catalogue
fatigue
gentle
jagged

Exercise 44
jagged
gentle
fatigue
catalogue
general
guide
guess
gust
Roger
vogue
rogue
germ

advantageous
pendulum
encouragement
juvenile
projection
education
cartridge
gradually
dangerous

arrange
league
lodge
vague

Exercise 46
1. guile
2. dialogue
3. fatigue
4. catalogue
5. intrigue
6. vogue
7. vague
8. League
9. guessed
10. guest

gesture
guilty
intrigue